PRODUCTION DICTIONARY

Terminology for those in Live Events,
Theater, Film and Concert Production

CARL BARNHILL
& LUKE MCELROY

COPYRIGHT

Published in Nashville, Tennessee through SALT Conferences, a division of Orange Thread Media, LLC.

For bulk, educational or organizational licenses, please contact Orange Thread Media for pricing and details.

Cover Design: [twelve:thirty]media
Book Layout: Douglas Williams
Edited by: Dan Almond and Tim Southwick

ISBN: 978-0-9913307-8-2

INTRODUCTION

This dictionary is an extensive guide of video, audio, lighting and other terms that are applicable to live events, theater, film, concerts and more. This resource will give you a quick reference guide to some of the most commonly used terminology used in production.

It is designed for both seasoned professionals, as well as those new to the events, film and theater industry. In some cases, some terms will vary depending on the country and region in which it is used.

Additionally, this resource includes a illustrated guide to connectors used in video, audio, lighting, power and networking.

CONTENTS

# #

1-SHOT
The camera framing of one subject; typically from the waist up.

1080I
A high-definition video format that has 1080 lines of vertical resolution and uses interlaced frames.

1080P
A high-definition video format that has 1080 lines of vertical resolution and uses progressive scanning frames.

16:9 ASPECT RATIO
Commonly referred to as "widescreen" format. The aspect ratio of High Definition video and measured by sixteen units wide by nine units high.

2-SHOT
The camera framing of two subjects within the same shot.

208V
The number of volts in a typical three-phase power system, calculated as the voltage between two hot phases of power.

3 POINT LIGHTING
The standard base for lighting a subject with a key light, fill light, and rim light. [1]

3-SHOT
The camera framing of three subjects within the same shot.

3G

An SDI cable that can carry a signal of 2.97Gbps which is conducive of carrying a 1080p 60fps signal.

4-CORNER

A phrase used when packing a truck or stacking cases that are heavy and require four people to each grab the handles in a corner and lift as a group.

4-HR MINI

Slang for "4 hour minimum" or the minimum amount of time a crew member will bill if brought out to the jobsite. Ex: they will bill for four hours even if they only work for 20 minutes. Usually after 4 hours, they are billed by the 15 or 30 min mark.

4:3 ASPECT RATIO

The traditional standard definition television aspect ratio measured by four units wide and three units tall. This aspect ratio is being replaced by 16:9.

4:3 SAFE

A method of shooting widescreen footage while still retaining a "safe area" that can be cropped and used for a 4:3 Aspect Ratio.

480I

The default standard definition video format with 480 lines of vertical resolution and uses interlaced frames.

4TH MEAL

After-show food provided to the crew following load out. Very common to be served on buses in concert tours.

720P

A high-definition video format that has 720 lines of vertical resolution and uses progressive scanning frames

A

A/B BUS An older video switcher configuration with 2 identical busses labeled A and B. If the A bus is live to screen, the next source desired is selected on the B bus. When the director hits the "take" button or dissolves on the T-Bar, the B bus becomes live to screen, and the A bus becomes available to select the next shot. This layout requires the operator to pay attention to which bus is live from shot to shot and has largely fallen out of favor.

A/V The abbreviation of "Audio-Visual" and can represent the elements of corporate production equipment. Ex: "I need to get all the A/V requirements together for the crew"

AC ADAPTER A circuit which modifies an AC Current, usually converting it to a DC Current

ADVANCE SHEET A document that outlines all the important information for a crew prior to a show including production schedule, lodging information, meal times (and locations), key personnel contact info and more details that relate to the crew. Also known as a front sheet, day sheet, or crew memo.

AIR WALL The movable barrier or temporary wall placed between large rooms to divide or separate into smaller space. This is most often seen in trade shows or hotel ballrooms where a larger ballroom can be separated into several smaller rooms. Most often, air walls are floating from the ceiling to avoid tracks or trip hazards on the floor.

AISLE   A passage through seating (often most common to allow people to walk between sections of chairs)

ALPHA KEY

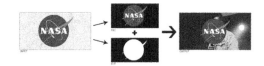

Also known as a Linear Key, this technology uses two outputs from a device, one as the "cut" and one as the "fill". The cut source is a separate video feed that just shows grayscale to identify the intensity of the object. When connected to a supported video switcher, the information received by the switcher from the grayscale source tells the switches to cut out those pixels from the fill source, and layer them on the screen.[2]

AMBIENT LIGHT   The light that spills over from other areas, or un-desired areas. Ex: when there is lighting coming in from a window or other room, this will cause ambient light when all other lights are off. Also known by some as "background light."

AMBIENT SOUND   Sound floating in the free air. In broadcast or streaming audio mixing, we are most concerned with ambient sounds from instruments, amplifiers, or monitors that might influence the balance of the mix.

AMMO CAN   The common storage container for truss bolts. See also bolt box.
[3]

AMP   This is the international unit of electrical current that flows through a conductor. Often symbolized by "A." One amp is equal to one volt applied across one ohm of resistance

AMPLIFIER Electronic sound device wired to the mixing board. It is used to increase the sound level put out through the speakers and monitors.

ANAMORPHIC A type of lens or adapter designed to produce a widescreen image from a condensed image on the film. Often used when needing widescreen in a 4:3 aspect video system.

ANSI LUMEN The common measurement of light output from a projector, measured by ANSI (American National Standards Institute). The higher the ANSI Lumen, the brighter the projector.

APERTURE A variable opening inside a lens that regulates the amount of light reaching the image plane. The aperture is also known as the iris.

APPLE BOX A wooden, often black, box or cube that is designed to raise a chair, person, or object to appear level on camera.[4]

APRON Section of stage that is in front of the proscenium and the downstage most portion of a stage. Also known as the Forestage, and often an extension of the stage into the audience.

ARRAY CALCULATOR A piece of software that allows a user to run a series of calculations to identify the angle at which a line array needs to be installed or set up.

ARRAY FRAME The structural header frame in which a line-array speaker system can hang with a chain hoist or shackle. Also known as a line array bumper.

ARS
Audience Response System, the term for any audience polling technology. The most common systems consists of a wired or wireless keypad with numbers, on which audience members can input their answer to a specific given question. Results can usually be displayed almost immediately after polling has concluded.

ART-NET
A lighting protocol allowing for control of multiple DMX Universes over ethernet. Art-net 4 was released in September 2016 and can support control of up to 1000 DMX ports (or 512,000 channels).

ARTIST TAPE
A moderately low adhesive tape that can be easily removed without leaving a residue or damaging the surface it was added to. Often this is white or lighter color, so you can easily mark with a pen or sharpie your notes. Also known as board tape.[5]

ASM
Abbreviation for Assistant Stage Manager

ASPECT RATIO
Describes the proportional relationship between a frames width and height. It is commonly expressed by two numbers separated by a colon. The standard aspect ratio of high definition is represented by 16:9 which is 16 units wide to 9 units tall.

ATMOSPHERE
This item is used to describe the mood in a room, often referring to the use of lighting, smoke and visual elements.

AUDIO INTERFACE

A hardware peripheral that allows a computer to connect to audio equipment. Audio interfaces can supply inputs to the computer, supply outputs from the computer's software to external audio devices, or most commonly, do both in one package.[6]

AUGMENTED REALITY (AR)

A simulated experience whereby visual technology is interactive in your real world environment, causing a blending of computer-generated graphic elements and the images seen through a camera, or lens.

AUTOMATED LIGHT

Also known as "moving light" or "intelligent light." This name refers to any fixture where multiple movement parameters can be remotely controlled.[7]

AUX BUS

1. (Video) An additional output bus to the main program bus that allows for mixing and routing of inputs in a more limited way than the switcher's primary output. Many switchers do not allow for transitions on the aux buses. Effects and keys often cannot be applied to aux busses.
2. (Audio) A secondary mix generated by an audio mixer or console. Aux busses are often used to create monitor mixes or route input signals to additional feeds or effects processors.

B

BACK FOCUS

The ability to fine-tune the adjustment of the distance between the lens and the camera sensor or chip. If back-focus is not set properly, the camera can look focused when you zoom in, and then lose focus when you zoom out. Often a focus chart will be the best tool to use when setting and refining backfocus.

BACKLINE

Musical instruments and related equipment used by musicians. It is not uncommon for backline to be rented locally when bands fly into a show.

BACK OF HOUSE (BOH)

Back of the house refers to the services and areas that an attendee does not see at an event. This includes catering kitchens, video world, loading docks, etc.

BACKLIGHT

A light which is positioned behind a subject. It's primary purpose is to make the subject stand out from the background by highlighting the subject's outline.

BALANCED AUDIO

An audio signal which consists of one "hot" signal plus one "cold" signal.

BALLAST

A container full of rocks, sand, shot, water, or cement that typically has a hook or anchor on the top to tie down tents, stages, or other structural elements.

BALLYHOO

The movement pattern of a lighting instrument when it resembles a figure-eight path in the air.

BANDING

A video glitch where dark bars appear across a displayed image in areas of movement on screen. Often caused by a signal interference, refresh rate inconsistency, or bad video processor.

BANDWIDTH

Bandwidth describes the maximum data transfer rate of a network or Internet connection. It measures how much data can be sent over a specific connection in a given amount of time. For example, a gigabit Ethernet connection has a bandwidth of 1,000 Mbps (125 megabytes per second).

BANQUET STYLE

A classic seating arrangement with round tables of 6-10 chairs for the primary purpose of dining or eating.

BANTAM CONNECTOR

Another term for the type of cable that is used when patching audio sources on a patch bay. This is technically a TT Cable, which stands for Tiny Telephone.

BARN DOORS

Rotatable metal attachment for a lighting fixture that contains 2-4 flaps on hinges, fixed to the front of a light for the purposes of blocking or shading light on a particular angle. Usually found on fresnel and wash lights to control the beam and block undesired light in a specific area on stage.

BARREL CONNECTOR

A small adapter to connect two cables of the same gender ends to each other. Often used when trying to extend a cable by attaching two cables together.

BARRICADE

A barrier between stage and the audience, often referred to as a security barrier. See also bike rack.

BASKET (RIGGING)

A rigging term to form a closed loop around something, such as an overhead beam by connecting two ends of a steel cable with a shackle so the loop does not tighten on the object, steel, or motor.

BATCH CAPTURE

The process of capturing multiple video clips automatically. A batch command is set up from the capture software which includes in and out points for each clip.

BATTEN LIGHT

A row or strip of lights in an single lighting fixture, often used to illuminate a flat panel or fabric with an even distribution. Also referred to as "strip light" or "bar light."

BATTEN PIPE

This is a pipe that lighting or AV equipmet can be attached to. Battens are usually hung above the stage and are most commonly seen in theatres.

BEAM CLAMP

An iron attachment device to hang something directly from the steel beam in a room or venue.

BEST BOY

The assistant chief lighting technician, often known in the film industry as a "key grip" or "gaffer". This person would often be in charge of scheduling the equipment and quantities of lights used for the production schedule of a film-shoot.

BIKE RACK

A barrier to prevent throughfare. Usually to contain crowds or audiences to not enter or pass certain area. See also Barricade.[8]

BIO BREAK

"Biological Break." A nice way of saying bathroom break. Often said as "Take a bio," as well.

BISCUIT (RADIO)
The slang term for a shoulder-mounted microphone and speaker for two-way radios. Also referred to as a Sling or Puck.

BITRATE
A calculation describing the amount of data that can be passed or transmitted per second along a network.

BLACK LEVELS
This is a reference to the contrast of an image and how deep the colors look. This can be adjusted on the camera body or control system for a camera to look more washed out or saturated.

BLACK WRAP
Metal flat tin-foil like material to prevent undesired light spill out of a fixture.

BLACKBURST
A form of genlock, and the technical term of a video waveform without the video elements. This includes vertical, horizontal and chroma sync information. Also referred to as "House sync."

BLACKOUT
A lighting cue that immediately brings the intensity of all lights to zero.

BLINDERS
Flood lights positioned on the audience to prevent spectators from seeing the stage during a scene change or moment during an event. Often used in rock concerts to "blind" the audience with a temporary burst of light from stage.

BLOCKING
The process of placing objects, people, or set pieces in a specific manner for the purpose of a live show. Often stage managers will be in charge of this in a corporate or entertainment show, and a director will dictate the blocking in a theatrical performance. In theatre, blocking tells actors and set designers where to move, place and interact with the elements on stage.

BNC
Stands for Bayonet Neill–Concelman, and is a common locking ring-like video connector for television production equipment. Most often found in SDI cables but can be seen in composite video cables, MADI digital audio cables, and radio antennas.[9]

BOARD TAPE
A moderately low adhesive tape that can be easily removed without leaving a residue or damaging the surface it was added to. Often this is white or lighter color, so you can easily mark with a pen or sharpie your notes. Also known as "artist tape."

BOARDROOM STYLE
This seating arrangement is often one large table, or a U-shape table with chairs on the outside to all participants can see the other and everyone has access to a table space in front of them. Often this is where discussion and brainstorming is the top priority.

BOLLARD
A metal or cement block in a parking lot that prevents traffic or vehicles from entering a specific area. Oftentimes, venues will need to "pull the bollard" or remove the barrier in order to allow trucks or crew into the loading dock or restricted areas. [10]

BOLT BOX
The common storage container for truss bolts. See also ammo can.

BONEYARD
Also known as "dead case storage" in a live event environment with temporary production elements. This is the area where empty cases after load-in are stored to be out of the way of other personnel or production elements.

BOOM   Also known as a Jib. A revolvable camera mounting arm, which can be attached to a dolly or crane to create a sweeping effect across an audience.[11]

BOOM LIFT   A work platform that is lifted by a jointed, bended arm structure. Also known as a cherry picker. [12]

BOOTH   Theatrical term for where front of house or the audio engineer and lighting director resides during a show.

BORDER CURTAIN   A horizontal and narrow piece of fabric that masks out the lighting instruments, antennas, or cable that are hanging from truss or pipe above the stage. This is often used in conjunction with leg curtains in order to provide a complete border on the top and sides.

BOWL   The common phrase for the audience that is in the lower raked sections of an arena or stadium. The term derives from the "bowl-like" shape of seating that surrounds the floor.

BOWLINE (KNOT)   A common knot in rigging which forms an "eye" at the end of a rope and is tied in the middle to create a loop that neither slips or jams. [13]

BOX LENS The slang term for a long-throw lens on a camera, usually containing a much higher quality glass. Also known as a large-format lens or sport lens.[14]

BRIDLE HANG (RIGGING) Using two beams to create one rigging point. The two points create a "V-like" design whereby the specific point is somewhere between the two beams.

BUCKET LIFT A vertical mast lift designed for use with a single operator that often have outriggers to counterbalance the weight. Also known as a single-man lift.

BUMP A flash or instant jump in brightness to a light or cue on a lighting console. Also known as a "flash" button.

BURLAP (RIGGING) This fabric or cloth is used in rigging to protect the steel beam or point from rubbing with the steel from the rigging apparatus.

BURN The process of recording information to an optical disk (CD or DVD)

BUS STOCK Items supplied for the talent's bus or green room. Typically includes ice, food/beverages, paper products, towels, etc. It is usually the responsibility of the event planner or promoter to take care of getting these items.

C

C STAND A general purpose grip stand used to hang lights, microphones, set pieces, or backdrops.[15]

C-CLAMP The type of mount on most lighting instruments used to attach a fixture to a truss, pipe or pole.

C-WRENCH An adjustable spanner wrench. Short for "Crescent Wrench."[16]

CABLE PICK A hang point dedicated to holding up a bundle of cabling.

CABLE RAMP A hard cover for cables used to protect cable from damage and to minimize trip hazards. Also referred to the brand name Yellow Jacket.

CABLE TIE A locking plastic strap used to hold cables, or other objects, together. Also referred to as "zip ties."[17]

CAD Short for "Computer-Aided Design;" Vector-based drawings of buildings, production designs or event details that are measured out to a specific scale. These are popular because of their ability to accurately get distances, heights, widths, and other measurements for a specific project.

CADDY
Slang term for rectangular flight case approximately 45" wide by 30" deep. Short for "cadillac case," which is commonly used in some areas of the country.

CALL TIME
The point in time you are required to arrive. This could be different for crew, talent, band or producers.

CAMLOK (OR CAM LOCK)
The most commonly used connector on feeder in the live production world. It is made up with a positive locking mechanism which makes for a secure connection and easy disconnection.[18]

CAMERA DOLLY
An apparatus upon which a camera can be mounted, which can be moved around smoothly.[19]

CANS
An informal term for headphones[20]

CARABINER
A spring loaded clip device to hook a cable, or wire.[21]

CARDIOID MICROPHONES
This directional microphone is designed to pick up audio from the front and sides, but not the rear.

CARNET
A document for international shipment of production equipment to a foreign country without having to pay duties.

CARTAGE

A fee charged to exhibitors for transporting freight from one point to another. Usually in union-controlled exhibit halls.

CATWALK

The platform where crew members can access lighting from the ceiling. Catwalks are often used in theatrical environments to allow crew to get to lighting truss without being seen by an audience.

CCU (CAMERA CONTROL UNIT)

This is a unit used to control the camera remotely (often operated by the Camera Shader or Video Engineer). It can control color, iris levels, black levels and more.

CG

Character Generator. This device puts text and graphics into a video signal that can be used to key over video or take full screen.

CHEESEBOROUGH

Also known as a pipe coupler or scaffold clamp, this allows for hanging various elements from pipe.[22]

CHOCK

A wooden block placed between two objects to prevent moving, shifting or a change in position due to the pressure of the block and object.

CHOKE

The term in rigging when you slide the end of one sling (or loop) through the eye of the opposite end, causing the cable to choke on the pipe or pole it's wrapped around.

CHROMA KEY

The process of replacing a particular color in an image with a different image. The blue and green hues are most commonly used for Chroma keying. This is often referred to as "green screen" or "blue screen."

CHYRON   A digitally generated title, lower third, graphic or superimposed image on a video. This name got its origin from the brand of superimposed images in the early days of television.

CLASSROOM STYLE   This seating arrangement is often composed of rectangular (often skinny) tables set up in rows with chairs behind them. This is idea for lectures, seminars, and meetings where note-taking or the use of computers is often beneficial. Attendees don't face one another at the table like banquet style.

CLICK PEN   A cleaning device for a fiber optic cable that uses a mechanical action to simultaneously rotate and push a cleaning tip into the connector of a fiber optic or smpte fiber cable.

CLICK TRACK   A prerecorded track of beats (like a metronome) to ensure proper musical timing for live performance. Often a channel in the rest of the backing tracks played by the band.

CLICKER   The slang term for presentation remote.

CLIPPING   The term used when an audio signal overloads the system and causes the signal to peak. This usually causes audio distortion on the source.

CLOVE HITCH   A common rope knot used in rigging to create a crossed hitch pattern by wrapping the pole or pipe twice causing the knot to be a secure bind due to tension in the rope. [23]

CMY   Abbreviation for Cyan, Magenta, Yellow color mixing to create different colors.

CODEC
A type of compression for data that enables a video, audio or other digital file to be transmitted faster and decompressed once received. The best example of this is the compression of video formats to be optimized for the environment whereby they are played back. ex: the codec h.264 is best for video played on the web.

COI
Abbreviation for Certificate of Insurance.

COLD SPARE
This is a backup piece of equipment that is not turned on until redundancy needs to be utilized. Ex: a cold spare can either be installed with signal but not power or it can remain in its case and live on-site in the event of an emergency.

COLOR BARS
A television test pattern, displaying vertical colored stripes (or bars). In the broadcast world, they are used to represent the head of a video tape to give consistent reference points during post production. As well, they allow easy color matching of cameras during a multi-camera shoot.[24]

COLOR TEMPERATURE
The color tint of a light source, represented in kelvin temperatures. A temperature with a higher number will appear more yellow and is often referred to as "warm" color temperature. A lower number temperature often has blue tones to its color, and is represented as a "cool" white. The color temperature of daylight is 5500k.[25]

COMPOSITE
The analog video signal format that carries standard definition on a single channel.

COMPRESSION
A process whereby audio or video data is re-calculated in a manner to consume less space and able to be transmitted over the internet or network faster. It reduces unnecessary data to achieve this lower file-size.

COMPRESSION TOOL
A special tool used to quickly and securely attach a connector, most often BNC or F-Connectors, by compressing the connector to the cable.

COMPS
A shortened common phrase for "complementary" and usually associated with free tickets given to crew or talent in a show.

CONCOURSE
The large open area in a public building or arena where the entrance is located. This is often the "main level" of a venue.

CONFIDENCE MONITOR
A downstage video monitor that most often doubles what's on the main projection screens. It us used to show the speaker or performer on stage what is on the screens so they don't have to awkwardly turn and look at the main screens. This is also known as "DSMs" or "down stage monitors" in some productions.

CONVERGENCE
The alignment of red, green and blue elements of a video chip or sensor to compose a single white line or point. The point at which all three colors is the ideal convergence for a clearly focused white pixel.

COVERAGE
A term used to describe how well sound covers an area.

CRAFT SERVICE
The term for where snacks, drinks or other small necessities are provided in a live production environment.

CRANK TOWER
A ground supported telescoping lift used to raise lighting systems, speakers, and scenery. Most crank towers have a weight capacity of about 500-600 pounds. Also known as a Genie tower.

CREW MEMO A document that outlines all the important information for a crew prior to a show including production schedule, lodging information, meal times (and locations), key personnel contact info and more details that relate to the crew. Also known as a advance sheet, front sheet, or day sheet.

CROSS HAIRS The plus pattern in a viewfinder of your camera that shows center.

CROSSFADE A video and/or audio transition in which one shot/clip gradually fades into the next.

CTB An abbreviation of color temperature blue, and a standard gel or color filter that turns tungsten lamps to "daylight" color by adding blue to the hue.

CTO An abbreviation of color temperature orange, and a standard gel or color filter that turns daylight lamps to a tungsten color by adding orange to the hue.

CUT An instantaneous transition from one shot to the next. "Take" may be used during camera direction to indicate a cut.

CYC LIGHTS A row of flood lights for illuminating the cyclorama or other backdrop on a batten.

CYCLORAMA Also known as "cyc" but pronounced "sike." A large fabric surface, usually white used as a background for the stage.

D

DAISY CHAIN   The process of connecting several pieces of equipment in a sequential order. This could be related to data, power or both.

DANCE FLOOR RAMP   This short (usually 6' long) ramp is useful when loading gear onto a shorter deck or space where a full truck ramp does not allow room. This name came from trucks that were built with a raised section in the nose of the truck, called the "dance floor."

DANTE   The brand name audio-over-IP interface whereby audio technology can be transmitted over standard ethernet with low latency on a multi-channel audio source.

DARK DAY   The slang term for a day during production or event that has no work or activity, often resulting in a day off of work, but required to be near the location of the event.

DAY SHEET   A document that outlines all the important information for a crew prior to a show including production schedule, lodging information, meal times (and locations), key personnel contact info and more details that relate to the crew. Also known as a advance sheet, front sheet, or crew memo.

DDR   Digital disk recorder. A stand alone unit that acts like a VTR, recording and playing video on a hard drive.

DEAD AIR   A concept where there is no activity, or sound, on a stage that is live. This is frowned upon in an environment as it results in a very awkward, silent, still environment

DEAD CASE STORAGE   Also referred to as Bone Yard. A designated area in a production to store cases once they've been unloaded or emptied.

DEAD HANG (RIGGING)   When a rigging point is attached directly to the grid or beam without a bridle or span.

DECIBEL (DB)   Logarithmic measurement of signal strength, often a measure of how loud sound is in a specific space.

DECK   Another term for a stage or platform.

DECK CHAIN   A specific chain made of grade 80 alloy allowing for up to 1200 pounds per inch and acceptable in concert rigging.

DEINTERLACE   The process of combining pairs of interlaced fields of video into one progressive frame of video.

DEPTH OF FIELD   The space between the nearest and furthest points at which the camera can obtain a sharp focus. Having "good" depth of field, allows for a start difference in focus between these two points, and can create the subject to appear on a nice blurred background. Depth of field is affected by aperture, ISO and the amount of light.

DESK   Slang term for console or control surface.

DHCP   An abbreviation for Dynamic Host Configuration Protocol. This is a network/internet term that helps prevent multiple IP addresses to be connected to the same network by configuring devices automatically with a unique identifier.

DI (DIRECT INPUT) BOX
A box that takes an input to create a balanced signal. This ensures low noise and a balanced output regardless of what the input device is (keyboard, guitar, or effects pad)[26]

DIGITAL VIDEO EFFECTS (DVE)
Effects (2d or 3d) applied digitally, either through a switcher's built-in processing capabilities or through an external system, to enhance the artistic features of video.

DIGITAL VIDEO RECORDER (DVR)
A device that captures video data onto a hard drive and can usually record and play video simultaneously, often with multiple channels.

DIGITAL ZOOM
The method of magnifying a subject on the screen with digital software modification and no moving optical or physical elements. This is an inferior method of zoom to optical zoom.

DIMMER BEACH
Where the lighting crew, dimmers and electrical panels are stored during a live event production.

DIRECTIONAL
Directional microphones are biased against sound from certain directions. The most popular form of directional microphone has a cardioid pickup pattern, which picks up sound from the front and sides, but rejects sound directly to its rear. Directional mics are very particular about placement, so care must be taken that the desired source is in the pickup pattern, and that unwanted sources are not.

DISSOLVE
A transition from one video signal to another in which one signal is fades down while the other is simultaneously faded up. The term "mix" is often used interchangeably with "dissolve."

DISTO　The generic term for a laser distance measurement tool, used to calculate the length between two points using laser technology.[27]

DISTRIBUTION AMPLIFIER (DA)　A device that allows the splitting of a single signal into multiple connections while amplifying the signal in each instance through an isolated output.

DISTRO　Slang term for Distribution Amplifier, and typically referring to the power distributor where all electrical cables will be converted from house power to show power.[28]

DMX　The standard for digital communication commonly used to control stage lighting and effects. Also known as DMX512 to represent the ability to carry information up to 512 unique channels or controls.

DOCK　A place where trucks load and unload gear and there is either an elevated area to push gear directly onto the truck, or some sort of lift system to make loading and unloading trucks easier than from the ground.

DONGLE　A slang term for a adapter that lives externally of a technological device.[29]

DONUT　A flat metal plate with a hole in the middle that attaches to a lighting instrument to sharpen the focus of a gobo, texture, beam or pattern.

DOORS
A term referring to when the public or audience will be let into the venue prior to the show starting. This will signify when the crew needs to be show-ready as an audience will now be in the room before an event starts. .

DOUBLE-STACK
Often when two or more projectors are placed on top of each other and aligned to make one screen. The benefits are for brighter images and redundancy with your projected image.[30]

DOWN RIGGER
The crew member(s) that stay on the ground during the rigging process and prepares the gear and ties to the rigger's rope. They also feed motor chains and organize/maintain the other rigging equipment before it goes up.

DOWNSTAGE

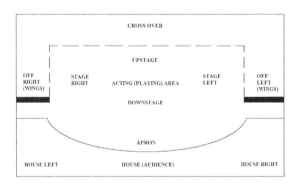

The area of stage closest to the audience. The center mark of the downstage area is often referred to as DSC or "downstage center."[31]

DOWNSTREAM KEYER (DSK)
A keyer that places a key after the MLE effects system output. This is known as "downstream" in the broadcast world, because it used to happen with a separate device. Now, most video switchers have them built in.

DRAYAGE   The concept in exhibit hall production where transport, storage and reloading of crates, trucks or containers when a show ends.

DROP FRAME   American system of time code generation that adjusts the generated data every minute to compensate for the spread of the NTSC television system running at 29.97 frames per second.

DRY AUDIO   The term used referring to raw or unprocessed audio signal.

DSM   Downstage Monitor, a television or display positioned downstage to show presenter or talent on stage a variety of information. Often this is used to show slides, clocks, time of day, or messages only visible by talent.

DUAL-LINK DVI   This format of DVI has twice the bandwidth of a single-link DVI and therefore can support higher resolutions.

DUVETEEN   A heavy black cloth, which is used for blacking out windows, masking set pieces, hiding cables, and hundreds of other uses. Also referred to by the slang term "duvey."

DUVEY   The slang term for Duvateen. A heavy black cloth, which is used for blacking out windows, making set pieces, hiding cables, and hundreds of other uses.

DVI   A cable connector type, abbreviated for "digital visual interface." This connection offers a locking mechanism most often used in video, computer and digital connections. There are two types of DVI: single-link and dual-link.

E

E-TAPE

Short for "electrical tape", made of vinyl usually and stretches well to give an effective adhesion for pressure-sensitive needs.[32]

E-TRACK

This horizontal (usually) or vertical system of slots that are perpendicular so that you can strap, tie down or control the elements within your truck. Using e-track ratchet straps, you can easily tie down equipment to prevent shifting of your cases or load while driving. Also see "e-track load bar."

E-TRACK LOAD BAR

This steel or aluminum bar mounts into the e-track system on a box truck or semi, to prevent loads or cases shifting while driving. They also are great to use if you have an uneven row of cases and need to start a new "wall" or fresh start to a truck pack.

EDID

Abbreviated for "Extended Display Identification Data" and is the data structure used by video displays to identify the desired or optional resolutions allowed on a specific device.

EDISON   Named for the inventor of the light bulb, the Edison connector is the standard 3-prong electrical connector on most standard household items. If the edison con-  nector can support 20 amps, one of the vertical blades will be perpendicular to the other.[33]

EDIT   The process of assembling video clips, audio tracks, graphics and other source material into a presentable package

EGRESS   The process or system to remove people, gear, crew, or other objects from an event. This may include closing down of roads, one-way streets, restricted access to specific areas of a venue or parking lot, and more.

ELLIPSOIDAL   Commonly referred to as a Leko, this is a profile lighting instrument with an elliptical reflector and at least one lens.[34]

EMBEDDED   The term used when video and audio are integrated in one cable or feed.

ENCODER   A hardware or software solution that accepts audio and video inputs from consumer, prosumer and professional devices for the purpose of formatting them correctly to be live streamed over the internet.

ENGINEER IN CHARGE (EIC)
The person on a crew who is the lead of video resolutions, sources, signal flow and refresh rates to ensure a universal system of power, signal and system design.

ENGINEERING CERTIFICATE
A document or license that the rig or structure has been submitted for approval from the chief rigging or engineering department of a venue. This is often required for use of production companies that wish to rig in a hotel or convention center.

ESTABLISHING SHOT
Usually a long shot at the beginning of a scene or moment in a show, which is intended to inform the audience about the setting, scene or location of what will follow. Especially during a broadcast or livestream environment to get context of the environment, set or atmosphere.

ETA
An abbreviation for "estimated time of arrival."

EVS
An abbreviation for the brand name product Eritrea Video Services, or a software based service that operates as a video replay or on-the-fly recording/playback for television production.

EXPENDABLE
The term used for items in production that are used once and then disposed of. (ex: tape, zip ties, rope, batteries, etc)

EXPOSURE
The amount of light which is passed through the iris.

EXTENDED REALITY (XR)
Term covering VR, AR, MR (Mixed Reality), that simulates an immersive environment whereby you don't know what is real, augmented or virtual due to it's seamless integration with the other.

F

F-CONNECTOR The plug used for coaxial cable. [35]

FADE Commonly used as an audio transition that dissolves from one source to another

FADE-TO-BLACK A controlled change of the on-air signal level down to the black level. Often new switchers include a "FTB" button now.

FALL ARREST A system designed to protect a rigger or crew member from falling when working in an elevated position. This system will contain a body harness, anchorage and a connector, and may include a deceleration device, lifeline or lanyard to protect against a fall.

FAN-IN An adapter that converts multiple individual connectors into a single multi pin connection

FAN-OUT An adapter that converts a single multi pin connector to several individual connectors.

FAT32 The standard way of organizing data on an external disk (like a USB Flash Drive) in a way that supports reading/writing on a mac and pc. This file format has a limit of 4gb for any individual file and can only be used for hard drives up to 2TB in total size.

FEATHER
To place an object in front of a light so that the edge of the light's output will be blocked, resulting in a blurred edge, and smoothly reducing the amount of light output.

FEEDBACK
An unwanted audio artifact caused by re-amplification of a signal. Most often in a live sound environment feedback occurs when a microphone picking up a source also picks up that source from the PA speakers. Feedback can occur at any frequency, but is most often associated with a shrill high frequency screech.

FEEDER
The wires connecting the transformer or company switch to the distro. These are usually 4-6 cables color-coded for their purpose with a neutral (white), ground (green) and three phases of hot (black, red and blue).

FIBER
A type of cable, whereby optical fibers are used (often fiberglass) to transmit a great deal of information over long distances in a virtually instantaneous period of time.

FIGURE-8 MICROPHONE
This bidirectional pickup pattern allows for capturing sound from two opposite sides of the microphone and best used when needing to capture sources from opposite angles, but nothing on the sides.

FILAMENT
The metal element of a light bulb that illuminates with electricity due to extreme heat. This glowing effect is what gives a light bulb the ability to be "light."

FLAG (FILM EQUIPMENT)
Also referred to as "cutters." They are usually metal, fabric or another material, designed to block specific light during a television or studio production environment. They are a large and manual version of barn doors.

FLAGGING

The act of waving your hand in and out of the beam of a light in order to identify where the light is positioned. This is most commonly used when focusing traditional fixtures.

FLAME RETARDANT

A compound used on fabrics or curtains where the material becomes resistant to a flame or fire. This is often required by the fire-marshall on all fabrics used in an environment with a live audience.

FLATS

A lightweight set piece often made of plywood, canvas, or other basic materials. They are used to create a "flat" wall when placed together or to create the various elements of a set design. They are often 4-8' wide, and sectioned to make moving them easy.

FLOAT

The term used in rigging when you raise the motors or hoists just enough to have the truss, poles or flown equipment float off the ground.

FLUID HEAD TRIPOD

A tripod head designed for video cameras. The head rides on a fluid chamber that allows for very smooth movements. Fluid heads are sold with a weight rating. To work correctly the total weight of the camera, lens, and all accessories mounted to the head must be under the rated weight.

FLY

The term used to rig, hang or suspend something in the air. Often a fly system comprises of pulleys, lever's and cables to allow the movement of objects in the air.

FLY OVER

During a pull or a push (camera movement), tilt the camera up and go over the subject's head to add an effect to the transition from one camera to the next.

FLYMAN

The operator of a fly system.

FLYPACK

A portable live event video camera setup including routers, cables, cameras, RCP, switchers, vectorscopes and more. Often this is used in portable environments to make setting up an I-MAG or Livestream more streamlined and time efficient.[36]

FOCAL LENGTH

The distance from the center of the lens to the camera.

FOCUS

The process of adjusting the lens in order to obtain a sharp, clear picture.

FOCUS CHART

A printed poster or sign that allows camera engineers to white balance and color correct the cameras all to a uniform white/pattern. This can also be used to set and refine the back focus of a camera.

FOGGER

Slang for Fog Machine. The device or piece of equipment that allows for large particles of dust, smoke or vapor into the air as a special effect. Low-Lying fog (fog that hugs the ground) can be created by cooling the fog as it exits the fogger. Closely related to a "hazer."

FOH (FRONT OF HOUSE)

This is where lighting, audio and some video personnel are placed. Usually, FOH is placed at the back of your auditorium or right under the front edge of your balcony. It's common that FOH is the best place to hear audio.

FOLD AND ROLL

A portable stage deck that can fold up in a way to place them vertically on two wheels.

FOLDBACK

Another term for Confidence Monitor.

FOLEY Sounds effects in videos that are made by mimicking an action with a prop that may not exactly match the action on screen.

FOLLOW SPOT A powerful lighting instrument that can be moved by an operator to provide a focused, extremely bright beam, onto the performance area highlighting the area it is aimed.

FOOT CANDLE A unit of measuring luminance equal to the light a candle outputs from one foot away. One foot candle is equal to one lumen.

FORK LIFT A vehicle with two pronged arms used to lift heavy loads, pallets or other cased equipment. [37]

FOURTH WALL The imaginary wall that lives between your subjects on stage and the audience in your room. Breaking the fourth wall is when an actor or subject acknowledges the audiences presence.

FPS Frames per second in video.

FR FABRIC An abbreviation for "flame retardant", or the classification given to a fabric that is not inherently resistant to flame and a chemical or additive has been used on the fabric to allow it to obtain a flame retardant certification.

FRAME The edges of a television, video, or film image. Also used to compose a camera shot.

FRAME RATE The number of individual frames per second on a film or piece of video. Most common frame rates are 24fps, 29.97fps, 30fps, 50fps and 60fps

FRAME SYNC   A digital time buffer used to align video signals that are not genlocked to the switcher. Many modern switchers include frame syncs, but many older switchers or professional broadcast switchers do not. In those cases there are external hardware frame syncs or option cards that can be used. If you have any sources in your system that cannot be genlocked, including computers, you will need a frame sync on those inputs. Some switchers will automatically engage a frame sync if they detect that they need to, on others it must be manually engaged per input.

FRESNEL   A light that has a stepped convex lens, allowing for better control than a par can. Often, the lights are a tungsten-incandescent lamp.[38]

FRONT FILL   Speakers that are usually placed on the front of a stage facing the audience to fill in for the inconsistencies of a line array style speaker system.

FRONT PROJECTION   When video is projected on the front-side of a screen surface.

FRONT SHEET   A document that outlines all the important information for a crew prior to a show including production schedule, lodging information, meal times (and locations), key personnel contact info and more details that relate to the crew. Also known as a advance sheet, day sheet, or crew memo.

FROST   A type of diffusion filter placed in a lighting instrument to soften the edges of the projected beam.

FULL SCREEN   Graphics that cover the entire screen.

FURNITURE DOLLY   A wooden or steel frame with wheels to make carrying heavy equipment easier. [39]

G

GAC FLEX
A round sling made up of strands of galvanized aircraft cable inside a polyester cover that is capable of hanging heavy weight loads. A gac flex is almost identical to a spanset, except that a spanset uses nylon fibers rather than aircraft cable.

GAFF TAPE
Also known as Gaffer's Tape. Designed with fabric on it's backing, and having an adhesive that is more heat-resistant allows this tape to be less susceptible to damaging surfaces. This is a more desirable tape in productions over duct tape.

GAFFER
A term in film production that represents the head of the lighting department and typically manages the electricians.

GAIN
The volume/amplification level of an audio or video signal. Also referred to the electronic enhancement of an image during low-light conditions to boost the camera brightness.

GAK OR GAC
The slang term used for miscellaneous stuff on a show that doesn't have a technical or universal name.

GAMMA
The setting on a video source to control the amount of luminance power on it's output. Without Gamma, shades of gray captured by digital cameras would not appear to our eyes, the way they appear on screen.

GATE An audio technique whereby the console or sound equipment will mute low level signals to improve the noise during pauses or unwanted moments.

GBPS Gigabit per second (symbol Gbit/s or Gb/s, often abbreviated "Gbps") is a unit of data transfer rate equal to: 1,000 megabits per second. ... 1,000,000,000 bits per second. 125,000,000 bytes per second. 125 megabytes per second.

GEL Pronounced "jel." This is a semi-transparent heat-resistant material which is placed in front of a light source in order to modify it's color and other characteristics.

GENIE TOWER A ground supported telescoping lift used to raise lighting systems, speakers, and scenery. Most Genies have a weight capacity of about 500-600 pounds. Also known as a crank tower.

GENLOCK The system or device that syncs two different video signals and ensures accurate timing of the frames per second. This enables various signals to be mixed together on a switcher or video router for seamless

GOBO A dark plate or screen to shield light output in a specific pattern or shape. Often used in relationship to Leko's or Ellipsoidal. This is also a term referring to the mask around a microphone or drum kit to shield unwanted sound out from microphones.

GOOSENECK 1. A flexible pole that is connected to a microphone stand and can move around freely.
2. The connection on a mobile stage or deck, that gets attached to a tractor for transportation.

GREEN ROOM A room located in a studio or concert venue, where artists and guests wait before their appearance.

GREEN SCREEN   Also known as "Chroma key." The process of replacing green in a film or video image with a different image in the post production process.

GRIP   The supporting crew member who cares for the cable on a camera operator or lighting operator where a cable may cause a hazard in the operator while in a live or recording environment.

GROUND LOOP   The hum or buzz found in an audio signal when the voltage of a power supply is found in the signal source.

GUI   Pronounced "gooey", and stands for the graphical user interface of a software or application. This is the screen or interface that a user will interact with on the front end of the software.

H

HALF PACK   Case size of 45" wide to allow for two cases to go side-by-side in a truck to fill the width. Each "half pack" case takes up one-half of the width of a 90" truck.

HAMPER   A cloth basket on wheels used in the live event world to carry soft-goods, fabric, curtain or sometimes other smaller cases.

HAZER   The device or piece of equipment that allows for dust, smoke or vapor into the air, allowing for an atmospheric element whereby you can see beams of light in the air. Closely related to a "Fogger" or Fog Machine.

HDCP   Abbreviation for High-Bandwidth Digital Content Projection, which is a digital rights management format that prevents the distribution or copying of audio and video content. It is a mandatory protocol for HDMI and optional for DVI.

HDMI   High-Definition Multimedia Interface. A digital connection used in video production and designed for primary use in home entertainment systems.

HEAD-TO-TOE   A term used by a video director to refer to a "full body" camera shot of a subject.

HEADLINER   "Largest" Artist performing at an event. Usually the highest paid and the last to perform. Often the main attraction to the entertainment or event.

HEADROOM The amount of space between the top of a subject's head and the top of the picture frame.

HERTZ A unit of frequency; describing the number of cycles per second. 1hz = 1 cycle/second.

HI VIS Short for "high visibility" and represents a fluorescent or reflective material to be seen well in a construction or active work site.

HIGH PASS FILTER (HPF) An audio filter which allows higher frequencies to pass through, thereby reducing lower audio frequency.

HOIST Generic term for a lifting device. See also motor or winch.

HOME RUN The term to describe the cable or signal route that is the last in line to the console, switcher, or final destination before being output.

HOT 1. An image or part of an image that is excessively bright or overexposed.
2. The wire in a cable, and the connecting pins, which carry a signal.
3. Refers to a camera shot that is live on your primary source or output.

HOT SPARE This is a backup piece of equipment that is turned on and running during an event to ensure redundancy without any delay. A hot spare is often no different than the object that is primarily being used and has signal and power running through it during operation

HOT SPOTS When a camera is raised too high you will see exploding areas of light where light is hitting an object.

HOT SWAP The changing of a plug, input, source or component without removing power to/from the device.

HOUSE

Refers to the entire venue, specifically the area where your audience or congregation sits.

HOUSE LEFT

The left side of an auditorium or venue determined by the audience's perspective looking at the stage.

HOUSE MUSIC

Background music or songs that are played during breaks or during pre/post show.

HOUSE RIGHT

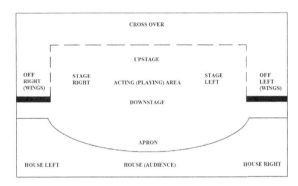

The right side of an auditorium or venue determined by the audience's perspective looking at the stage.[40]

HUE

The characteristic of color signal that determines whether the color is red, yellow, green, blue, purple, etc. (The three characteristics of a TV color signal are chrominance, luminance and hue.) White, black and grey are not hues.

HUMBUCKER

A Transformer used to isolate video signals caused by interference from bars or morie.

HYPERCARDIOID MICROPHONE

The directional microphone that has a more defined polar/pickup pattern where it is most sensitive to an on-axis audio source. Also known as a supercardioid microphone

I

I/0 The in and out connections, cables or ports of a technical device.

I&D Shorthand for "installation and dismantle" and a term used in exhibit halls for setup and teardown.

IATSE Abbreviation for International Alliance of Theatrical Stage Employees, and is the union that represents the crew members and technicians in stage, film and television production. Usually in a live production environment, if you were to hire local labor, they may be from the local IATSE crew.

IEC CONNECTOR The standard power connector on computer supplies, and misc power supplies of electronic equipment. IEC stands for International Electro-technincal Commission, and standardized international uses of A/V Technology

IEM An abbreviation for "in ear monitors." An audio monitoring system for people on stage that uses earpieces rather than large stage monitor speakers.

IFR FABRIC An abbreviation for "inherently flame retardant", or the classification given to a fabric that is resistant to a flame or fire without any additionally added chemicals or elements.

IMAG Short for "Image Magnification" and is when you take a camera shot and display them on screens in the venue or auditorium.

IMPEDANCE — Electrical resistance in AC circuits.

IN-POINT — The beginning of an edit or transition.

INCANDESCENT LIGHT — This is the type of lamp used in most conventional lighting fixtures. It creates light through a glowing filament

INTELLIGENT LIGHTING — Special lighting instruments controlled by a computer to move, change color, flash, etc. with a pre-designed program. Also referred to as moving lights or automated lights.[41]

INTERCOM — A 2-way audio communication system that allows production crew members to talk to each other in real time. Often intercom is wired (although it can be wireless) with a headset that includes headphones and a microphone all in one.

INTERLACED VIDEO — A method of displaying video where odd rows of pixels are drawn first, then even rows. A video is written from top to bottom alternating every row on pixels, happening many times per second.

INTERMITTENT — Occurring at irregular intervals; not continuous or steady. An intermittent video or audio signal is one that is not stable in their feed or source. This could refer to a video or audio signal that stops and starts at periodic, or random, intervals without any cause or reason.

IPV4 — The standard version of an internet protocol, or IP addresses defined by four sections of three digits each. Each three digit number can be between 0 and 255. (ex: 111.111.111.111)

IRIS   The ring on the camera that controls the aperture, the aperture controls the amount of light that the camera lens lets in so the image doesn't get washed out or too dark.

ISO   Short for isolation. In video, this means you record an individual, isolated, source as a separate recording of that from your program mix. In audio, this may be to used to identify the specific sound in a mix, ex: "lets iso that to see where it is coming from."

ISP   Abbreviation for Internet Service Provider, or the way in which you can access an internet connection. (ex: Comcast)

J

JIB

A revolving camera mounting arm, which can be attached to a dolly or crane. Also known as a Boom.[42]

JITTER

An intermittent video signal that appears to shake due to its unstable image quality.

JUICER

A slang term in the film industry for an electrician

JUMP CUT

A video transition in which one shot appears to "cut" to another shot with very similar framing.

JUMPER

Slang term for a short extension cord, typically made in five-foot increments, starting at one foot.

K

KABUKI
A type of curtain drop that allows an instantaneous release of pins or hooks to cause a curtain, fabric or screen to fall at the push of a button.

KELVIN
A unit of measurement used for absolute temperatures and color temperatures.

KERNING (TYPOGRAPHY)
The horizontal space between individual characters in typography. Kerning is usually defined by the font family, but helps separate the lowercase "f" in a different spacing than the letter "o" since they take up different positions next to each other.

KEY
An effect produced by "cutting a hole" in a background video, then filling the hole with video or matte from another source. Alpha or Key source video cuts the hole; fill video fills the hole. The video signal used for cut and fill can come from the same or separate sources.

KEY LIGHT
The main light on the subject, providing most of the illumination and contrast

KEYNOTE
1. A speaker at an event that is the main draw or is top billed.
2. That speaker's actual speech or timeslot.
3. Apple's presentation software.

KEYSTONE   A distorted, trapezoid-like effect, of an image when the edges are not the same dimension of the opposite side, creating a tapered or wedge shape.

KILL   To strike, remove or turn off.

L

LADDER TRUSS A flat 2-dimensional truss structure that allows you to hang lighting fixtures on top of each other in a vertical array.

LAN Abbreviation for Local Area Network. This technology connects the devices, computers and systems that are all on the same geographical location. A LAN does not have to have internet access.

LAVALIER MICROPHONE A microphone that clips onto a lapel or shirt. Also revered to as Lav or Lapel microphone. Often paired with a wireless mic transmitter for a hands-free, mobile solution.[43]

LEAD-ROOM The amount of space between the subject and where they are looking.

LEADING (TYPOGRAPHY) The horizontal space between the baseline of a character in typography. Unlike kerning, which separates specific letters differently based on their design structure, leading changes the space between all characters equally.

LED Stands for "Light Emitting Diode" and is a common type of light that can be used in lighting fixtures or video walls.

LEFT THIRDS Graphics that take up the left third of the screen

LEG CURTAIN

A vertical piece of fabric that masks out the sides of a stage. This fabric is often black and hung to distinguish on-stage and back-stage areas, while covering activity, props, equipment or people standing slightly backstage.

LEKO

Slang for an Ellipsoidal. This is a profile lighting instrument with an elliptical reflector and at least one lens.

LENS

A transparent structure made of glass and other materials, with at least one curved surface, which causes light rays passing through it to converge or diverge in a controlled fashion.

LETTERBOX

When the aspect ratio is shorter height-wise, there are additional black boxes on top and bottom of the frame. These black areas are called letterboxing. Most often then a 16:9 aspect ratio file is played on a 4:3 frame.

LIGHTING CONSOLE

A board used to control all of the lighting effects used on stage. They are usually placed out in front of the stage near FOH.

LIGHTING PLOT

A predetermined plan of where lights and connectors will be placed in a show. Often the lighting plot will specify the lens, lamp, fixture type, cable paths, and DMX addresses of the lights identified on a live show.

LINE ARRAY

A loudspeaker system that is made up of identical boxes in a line, fed in phase to create a line of sound.[44]

LINE ARRAY BUMPER

The structural header frame in which a line-array speaker system can hang with a chain hoist or shackle. Also known as an array frame

LINE LEVEL   The nominal signal level generated by an audio console or processor. Most typically this is +4dBu.

LINE OF SIGHT   Refers to what the audience can see in a direct line from where someone is sitting. Often referred to as well by the direction a light or projector is aimed.

LINEAR KEY   A keying process that uses 2 signals, cut and fill, to layer the image. The cut signal is created based on transparency in the graphic source. Also known as an Alpha key.

LIP SYNC   The term used to match lip movement from a video feed or file to the voice or audio feed.

LIVE   A term used by a video director to refer to the camera that is on program or one that is on the main projection screens.

LIVE STREAM   A transmission of visual or auditory formats in real-time over the internet

LOAD RATING   The maximum amount of weight a piece of rigging equipment can safely lift. Often marked as WLL (Working Load Limit.)

LOADER (UNION)   The union stagehand(s) that are responsible for loading a truck. In some states/locations, loaders and pushers have to be two different people.

LOOM   A collection of separate cables bound together for convenience.

LOOSEN UP   A term used by a video director to get a camera operator to zoom the camera out just a little bit to create a wider shot of the subject.

LOSE LEFT   Pan the camera left to lose the subject out of frame

LOSE RIGHT	Pan the camera right to lose the subject out of frame
LOW PASS FILTER (LPS)	An audio filter which allows lower frequencies to pass through, thereby reducing higher audio frequency.
LOWER THIRD	The lower portion of a video frame which contains graphical information such as name/title, social media handles, text or other content.
LTL	A trucking term that stands for "less than truckload" and represented a shipping method that means your truck may not be dedicated and will likely include additional materials from another customer.
LULL	A specific brand of fork-lift, but often referred to a fork lift that is larger and can drive through rough terrain. These are often used in festivals or outdoor events where cases need to be taken from trucks to stage decks without smooth or finished ground.
LUMA KEY	

A keying process that is targeted to black. Anywhere that black appears in the program image will be replaced with the key source content.[45]

LUMEN	A measurement of light output. See ANSI Lumen for light output of a projector.
LUMINANCE	A measure of brightness.

M

MACRO
A sequence of programmable events that can be recalled to automate common, complex or creative tasks.

MADI
Stands for Multichannel Audio Digital Interface. A standard that allows for transmission of multiple channels of audio over coaxial, catagroy, or fiber optic cable. The most popular configuration allows tranmission of 64 channels of audio at 48kHz.

MAGIC HOUR
The minutes just around sunset and sunrise, where light levels change drastically and quickly, lending a warm orange glow to earlier shots, and a clearer blue in later minutes that allows a crew to shoot night scenes while light still remains.

MAGS
A slang term for "Magnetometer", or the security device used at most venues to detect for metal on a patron or ticket holder.

MARK
A shorthand phrase for identifying where something will be positioned or placed. This is used most often in "mark the floor." Also referred to as spike mark.

MARLEY (FLOORING)
A type of staging surface that can be reflective or matte and made of a vinyl material which is common for use with dancers or sport use. They are often what cause a stage to seem highly reflective or glossy.[46]

MARLITE
One-time use shiny, reflective, flooring material that is fixed to a stage deck for a temporary amount of time. It's common that Marlite comes in 4'x8' sheets. This is often a far more afford-able version of marley.

MARSHALING YARD
The location where trucks need to check in be-fore delivering to a dock or exhibit hall.

MASK
A digital method of preventing a projected image from showing up in places it shouldn't. Typically this is achieved in a software that can lay a black and transparent object on the upper most layer.

MASONITE
A specific type of hard board material often placed on event floors to protect, disperse weight or allow for easy rolling of cases, etc.

MATRIX
An electrical device that accepts and distributes video or audio signals from multiple inputs and multiple outputs.

MEAT RACK
A rack on wheels that often transports pre-rigged lights, bars, truss or set pieces.

MIC LEVEL
The nominal input signal level generated by a microphone, typically about -50dbu. Mic levels need to be amplified to raise them to line-level.

MICROPHONE
Also known as "mic", used to relay sound from the stage to the sound system by amplifying the noise that it captures and converts to an electrical current. These can be wired or wireless.[47]

MID-SHOT   A camera framing term, half-way between a wide-shot and close-up shot. A mid-shot of a person will show them from the waist up.

MIDI   Stands for "Musical Instrument Digital Interface." It's a standard communication between musical voice or instrument sound.

MIL   The distance between two pixels on an LED Wall. This defines the resolution, pixel density and sometimes brightness of an LED wall. The lower the number, the higher the resolution. (ex: 4.2mil led walls)

MINI WECO   The specific type of cable & connector used to patch video signals in a video patch bay.

MINIDV   A consumer-level digital video format.

MINUTE BY MINUTE   Another term for a production timeline, showing what is happening at every stage of an event and who is responsible.

MIXER   A device which accepts multiple signal inputs (video or audio), processes them, and provides one or more outputs.

MIXING   Term refers to changing the volume and mix of each channel of sound being used for a show. Includes making variations in the high, mid, and low tones of music and vocals.

MLE   An abbreviation for multi-layer effects.

MOIRE   An undesired video artifact caused by fine patterns or textures being captured poorly by a digital camera sensor. Moire often appears as curving, often rainbow colored, lines through the image. Quality lenses, sensors, and higher resolutions can all help avoid moire.

MONITOR
1. A device used to view a video, graphic or text source.
2. An audio term used for speakers on stage so the performer can hear themselves.

MONITOR WORLD
The location where an engineer and a console is used to control the specific levels in the monitor wedges or IEMs of a performer. This is usually located just offstage in a position where the performers can see and/or communicate with the sound engineer easily without obstruction.

MOTOR
This is the generic term for an electric chain hoist whereby a point is fixed. The most common sizes are 1/4 ton, 1/2 ton, 1 ton and 2 ton, referring to the weight that motor point can hold.

MULT BOX
Also referred to as a Press Mult or Press Feed, this box helps distribute multiple audio and/or video connections to additional recorders for the purposes of giving press or external recording teams access to broadcast audio.

MULTI-VIEW
A custom view created by a switcher or hardware multi-view processor that shows multiple video sources at once, typically in a grid layout. Most video switchers can generate a multi-view that shows all  input sources as well as output busses, allowing the operator to see all available camera shots and choose them as needed.[48]

MULTIMETER
An electrical instrument to measure current, voltage and resistance in a cable, plug, outlet or electrical connection.

MULTIPLEX   An electrical connector that carries 19-pins and allows for multiple power lines to be run within one single cable. This type of connector is a standard in stage lighting and video technology whereby multiple electrical signals are needed in one place. There are also breakouts to go from multiplex to edison, stage pin, and power-con. Also referred to as the brand name Socapex.

N

NDI

An abbreviation for network device interface, which is a royalty free video standard whereby video can be transmitted over a network or internet protocol. This is not the same as video over cat5.

NEAR FIELD MONITORS

Speakers that are used for monitoring or critical listening very close (within 3-5 feet) to the user. Near field placement can help reduce the effects  of the room the listener is working in, aiding in creating more accurate mixes.[49]

NEUTRAL DENSITY (ND) FILTER

Colorless filters that reduce the amount of light in controlled degrees. Often used when trying to balance the amount of light in an outdoor shoot when balancing a blue sky and a subject.

NON-LINEAR

Any method of video editing which doesn't require all shots to be assembled in a linear fashion.

NTSC

Stands for "National Television Standards Commission" and refers to the standard broadcast format for the USA, Canada, Mexico and other major countries. It delivers 525 horizontal lines of resolution at 30 fps.

O.T.	Abbreviation for Overtime

OFF-LINE	A file, media or object that is out of action, not currently usable.

OMNI DIRECTIONAL	Often used to describe the pickup pattern of a microphone. An omni-directional microphone will be sensitive to sound in all directions. Omni-directional microphones tend to be very natural sounding.

ON-DEMAND	A transmission of visual or auditory formats on the internet where the user can scrub, pause, fast forward, rewind or stop without losing access to content. This is not often used with real-time transmission

OPTICAL ZOOM	A mechanical system that uses physical lenses to magnify a subject for the camera sensor. This is preferred over digital zoom.

OPTO SPLIT	Common term for an optical splitter used to distribute multiple DMX feeds.

OUT-POINT	The end point of an edit.

OVERCRANKING	Shooting in a frame rate that exceeds the actual playback, resulting in a slow motion effect.

OVERSCAN	The result of the television scan lines exceeding the boundaries of the display screen causing information to be cut or cropped off.

P

PACKET Data sent over a network, LAN or internet source.

PACKET LOSS The amount of data that is lost or dropped during a stream or transmission of data over the internet or network.

PAL Known for "Phase Alternating Line" and is the European color television standard that specifies 625 lines per frame at 25Hz.

PAN 1. Video term describing horizontal camera movement. Moving your camera left or right.
2. The audio term for moving sound in a stereo setup from left to right.

PAN LOCK This adjustment prevents the tripod from moving side to side when an operator isn't present or if the operator doesn't need to pan.

PAR Stands for "Parabolic Aluminized Reflector" and is a common lighting instrument that contains a filament, reflector and lens in one unit.[50]

PARAMETRIC EQ An audio equalizer having multiple parameters to control for various bands/frequencies of audio.

PASSBOARDS
A poster or board showing all the backstage passes that are allowed in specific areas. Often, concert tours or festivals will print these and scratch out which passes can't go to the area that security guard is standing at. This ensures that communication is clear for security personnel.

PEAK
The highest level of strength of a signal. If the "peak" or "clip" light on an audio mixer is activated, this means the respective bus (channel) is peaking at a dangerous level.

PER DIEM
The amount of money provided to crew to cover daily expenses like food, transportation and miscellaneous personal expenses. Often per diem is a daily charge or allocation of money provided to a crew member when elements like meals or transportation is not reimbursable.

PERFECT CUE
A brand name clicker or presentation remote that uses radio frequencies instead of bluetooth or IR technology and therefore is far more reliable. This is the standard presentation remote for professional events

PERIPHERAL
An external device that can connect or provide additional functionality for a computer or piece of technological equipment. For example, an input card on a switcher, is a Peripheral.

PETTY CASH
This is a float pool of money used for runners, errands, or other misc needs on the day of a production.

PHANTOM POWER
A means of distributing a DC current through audio cables to provide power for microphones and other equipment.

PHASING
In audio, this is an effect where wave interactions create various sweeping sounds as the waves of two different sources cancel each other out.

PICK LIST

A sheet or document that outlines all the equipment needed for a show or event. This is usually produced by the warehouse manager or production manager and helps determine what equipment needs to be loaded onto a truck or pulled/picked from the shelves. Also known as a pull sheet.

PICKLE

A controller for a single chain motor

PINK NOISE

A sound signal that has an equal amount of energy per octave or fraction of an octave. Used as a test and calibration signal.

PIP

Known for "picture in picture." Which is technology that allows one video signal to be layered over another video signal or graphic element. Most often seen in the context of panoramic screens where IMAG is layered on a background or other imagery.

PIPE & DRAPE (P&D)

A portable system of fabric and poles (both crossbars and uprights) to provide masking, backdrops, and/or décor in a live environment. These sectional and temporary elements of drape or fabric are often adjustable in their width and height.[51]

PIXEL

Short for "Picture Element." A pixel is a single dot of a video image or graphical image. The total number of pixels represent the resolution of a visual element.

PIXEL MAP

The output raster of an LED wall, projection mapping surface or custom video wall to define the number of pixels, and their layout. This is useful for the screen control, VJ and content producers to know where, and how, the video surfaces will be laid out as well as their respective pixel counts.[52]

PIXILATION

Visual square-like digital noise that appears on a monitor when playing back a lower resolution on a higher resolution output.

PLUMB LASER

The specific laser used in rigging to produce a single dot in the air. This is usually placed on the ground where the motor point needs to live, and helps riggers know where to attach the steel or points in the air.

PM

Abbreviation for Production Manager, or the individual in charge of the production logistics, crew, gear and production schedule.

POINT-TO-POINT

The concept of live streaming or video conferencing between two locations without broadcasting to a public website or service. One end has an encoder, and the other(s) have decoders.

POLARITY

The positive (above the medium line) and negative (below the medium line) peaks of the audio waveform. When you flip the waveform, you create negative polarity.

POV CAMERA

Short for "point of view" and uses when a camera operator can't be in the location of a camera. Sometimes referred to as "lipstick" cameras because of their size, but often are unmanned as they're mounted to truss, helmets, railings, ceilings, vehicles, etc.

POWER AMPLIFIER

A device which accepts a relatively low level audio signal (line level, +4 dBu) and boosts it to a level (speaker level, +25 dBu) at which it can be output to a loudspeaker.

POWER-CON

An electrical connector manufactured by Neutrik for connecting power in a small, confined space. It works similar to the speakon connector, with the line connector inside a chassis that can twist and lock.[53]

PPE Abbreviation for Personal Protective Equipment, and the equipment needed to protect yourself on an event. This may include steel toe boots, protective headgear, gloves, etc.

PRE-RIG The concept of hanging elements of rigging before the production crew arrives at the venue.

PREAMPLIFIER (OR PREAMP) An electronic device that boosts extremely weak mic level signal voltages, such as those from microphones or mag heads, to line level (+4 dBu) for use with audio mixers, processors, and power amplifiers.

PRESENTATION REMOTE The device used by a speaker, presenter or talent where they can wirelessly trigger or signal the advancement of a slide/graphic.

PRESIDENTIAL TELEPROMPTER The specific teleprompter that have computer screens on the ground near a podium, and small glass plates in front of the speaker, cause the teleprompter to be reflected, in a way where cameras cannot see the script.[54]

PREVIEW (PVW) A switcher output that shows the scene that will go on-air when the next automatic or manual transition takes place.

PREVIEW/ PROGRAM BUS The default bus configuration for modern video switchers. The program bus is solely dedicated to the live output, and the preview bus is solely dedicated to assigning the next source for the "take" button and T-Bar. When the user takes a shot the preview bus selection becomes live on the program bus, and the former program bus selection becomes the current preview bus selection.

PRODUCER   The crew member who runs the live show and often calls the cues over intercom. They are often responsible for leading the entire team of people who are operating the production and the lead person on a production.

PRODUCTION SCHEDULE   A detailed plan of activities associated with the live event, film project or service that often includes meals, load-in details, rehearsals and other primary activities.

PROGRAM (PGM)   The on-air output of the video system.

PROGRESSIVE VIDEO   A method of displaying video where rows of pixels are written on screen in order, or progressively, from top to bottom. Since progressive scan video displays all the rows at a time, rather than half the rows like interlaced, it's usually a higher quality than interlaced.

PROMPT BOOK   In theatrical productions, the stage manager's copy of the script that shows blocking notes, technical cues and other information will be compiled into the "prompt book."

PROSCENIUM   In a theater the proscenium is the opening in the wall at the front of the stage, usually where the main curtain is hung.

PTZ CAMERA   A camera on a motorized mount that allows remote control of Pan, Tilt or Zoom functions.[55]

PUCK (RADIO)   The slang term for a shoulder-mounted microphone and speaker for two-way radios. Also referred to as a Biscuit or Sling.

PULL   A term used by a video director to get a camera operator to widen your shot out slowly for an effect.

PULL SHEET   A list or document that outlines all the equipment needed for a show or event. This is
usually produced by the warehouse manager or
production manager and helps determine what
equipment needs to be loaded onto a truck or
pulled/picked from the shelves. Also known as
a pick list.

PUSH   A term used by a video director to get a camera
operator to zoom in your shot slowly for an
effect.

PUSHER (UNION)   The union stagehand(s) that are responsible for
pushing cases into the truck. In some states/
locations, pushers and loaders have to be two
different people.

PYROTECHNICS   The use of explosives, fire or lasers in the
course of an event. Most counties require them
to be run by a licensed pyrotechnician.

Q-BOX   An all-in-one audio cable tester with the ability to hear and generate a tone through a cable.

QUAD BOX   An outlet that has four plugs; usually seen on concert stages for artist power needs or audio inputs.

QUARTER PACK   Case size of 22.5″ wide to allow for four cases to go side-by-side in a 90″ to fill the width. Each "quarter pack" case takes up one-fourth of the width of a truck.

QUARTZ   Tungsten-Halogen lights or lighting units. The name is derived from the material which encloses the lighting element.

R

RACK FOCUS   Purposely going in and out of focus for an effect.

RATCHET STRAP   Also known as a truck strap, but used to secure cargo inside trailers, or against other objects for the purpose of transport. These are also used to help secure an object to a truss or pipe like Scrims, tents and signage from blowing away. Also known as "motorcycle strap."[56]

RCP   Remote Control Panel or Remote Control Paint-box. A control station that ties into a Camera Control Unit (CCU) to remote access to camera parameters and settings including iris, color settings, and menu selections. In a professional broadcast setting a video engineer's station will include a color accurate monitor and an RCP for every camera allowing the engineer to perfectly match the color and exposure of each camera.

READY   Another phrase for "Standby" used often by a camera director. This alerts camera operators or graphics operators to setup a shot or image before going live on program.

REAL TIME   Anything which occurs without delay. A real time effects processor will add effects instantly, without having to wait to render.

REAR PROJECTION   When video is projected on the back-side of a screen surface.

RECLOCKING   Reclocking allows you to reset the sync between video signals and boost their signal for additional length. Technically, reclocking syncs the amplitude, rise and fall times, and clock rate attributes of a digital signal.

REEFER TRUCK   Slang term for refrigerated box truck.

REFRESH RATE   The frequency at which an image is refreshed on a display, screen or monitor. This is usually measured in hertz.

RESET   A phrase used by a camera director to get a camera operator to start your shot over again from the beginning.

RESOLUTION   The amount of detail and pixels in an image or signal.

REVERBERATION (OR REVERB)   The amount of time it takes an emitted sound to cease bouncing off objects such as walls. In audio, adding reverb gives the sound more body and can make it seem as if the recording was in a large room or hall.

REVERSE SHOT   A camera framing term that helps the operator know to take a shot from behind the subject.

RF   Short for "Radio Frequency" and applies to the spectrum of wireless equipment that requires radio transmission.

RGB   Abbreviation for Red, Green, Blue color mixing to create different colors.

RIDER   Information sent to a venue by a touring production that details requirements for lighting, audio, rigging, and other technical elements. Will also include specifications for dressing rooms and other accommodations to be provided by the venue.

RIGGER
Someone who is responsible for hanging equipment above the stage or over the audience. These certified individuals are used to ensure the safest way to harness a large object over the heads of people or other objects.

RIGGING PLOT
A diagram or drawing showing where the motor or hoists are to be positioned in a grid for use when pre-rigging or rigging a production.

RIGHT TO WORK
The classification of a state whereby a person cannot be denied work because of membership or lack thereof to a labor union.

RIM
A hard backlight, generally on the same level as subject, that casts more light than the key light.

RISER
A form of stage decking that can raise the level of something on your stage. Typically used to refer to the platform that a drummer or keyboard player performs on.

ROAD CASE
A storage device used in live events that can withstand the regular use of load-in, load-out and transportation while protection of the gear within. Most road cases have wheels for easy transport. May also be called a flight case or ATA case.[57]

ROTOSCOPING
An animation or post-production process of tracing the image of a moving object (either manually or automatically) to place them on another background.

ROUTER
A hardware device that has multiple in and out ports that can send data from one connection to another or multiple. This acts as a hub of connections for most areas of production and can provide easy access to changing feeds and their sources without the need of an additional switcher that will frame-sync the inputs and outputs together.

RTA The abbreviation for "real-time analyzer", the device that measures the frequency of audio in a room using an integrated microphone or the signal from your PA[58]

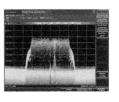

RTMP The abbreviation for "Real Time Messaging Protocol." A protocol that allows streaming audio and video content over the internet. Many streaming services use RTMP to transport H.264 encoded video.

RULE OF THIRDS A technique in camera framing where the frame is divided into imaginary sections to create reference points for composition sake.

RUN OF SHOW (ROS) The piece of paper or online format that shows details of every cue in a production. It's the primary document used by the crew, talent, and producers to identify and communicate what is supposed to happen at every moment in time with a live event, including specific detail on audio, lighting and video cues.

RUN OUT (RIGGING) The concept in rigging of running the motor of a chain hoist to remove all excess chain before putting the motor in the case. This is standard practice to ensure the length of the chain is the maximum distance to make hanging the motor point in the next venue easier.

RUN THROUGH Another term for rehearsal.

RUNNER A person who is responsible for running errands for talent or crew on the day of the event. Most often this is requested to be a local with good knowledge of the area and a clean driving record.

RUNNING LIGHTS Dim lighting backstage (usually blue) that allows the cast and crew to see while the stage and audience are dark.

S

SAFE AREA Often marked on a viewfinder of a camera by a box that just a few pixels inside the frame, to show what area is safe for all televisions to show. Also known as "viewing area"

SAFETY A chain or wire that is fixed to a light or technical instrument to prevent it from dropping off a truss or pipe in the event that a clamp fails. Often they have a hook carabiner on one side with a metal wire with a loop at the alternate end. It is standard practice to place a safety cable on every fixture that is attached to a truss or pipe with a clamp.

SAMPLE RATE The number of times in an audio file that sound is "sampled" or the frequency in a digital recording. The most common sample for CD audio is 44.1khz.

SANDBAG A bag that is made of canvas and filled with either sand or weighted lead pebbles and have a handle in the middle for easy carrying. Also known as "shot bags" in the film world.

SCAFFOLDING Steel structures used to support risers, decking, stage, or sound systems. [59]

SCISSOR LIFT A work platform that is lifted by a cross-braced understructure.

SCOOP LIGHT   A large dome-like reflector light that acts as a floodlight without a lens to focus the light.[60]

SCREEN CONTROLLER   The position on a crew that operates the technology to determine the inputs and sources on a variety of different outputs. Often this crew member will use a Spider or Encore system to manage multiple resolutions, inputs, outputs and/or formats in a method to route these signals to the right moment in a live show.

SCRIM   Light-weight, often somewhat translucent, woven cloth or covering used for decorative purposes. If lit appropriately from the front with no back light, a scrim can be seen as a backdrop and hiding activity that takes place behind the curtain. However if lighting is entirely behind the scrim, the fabric can be perceived as transparent.

SCROLLER   A lighting instrument attachment, controlled by DMX, that can scroll through several different gel colors.

SDI   Stands for "Serial Digital Interface" and is a uncompressed digital video signal sent down a single coax line providing stunning digital quality over long runs. SDI standards also allow for up to 16 channels of uncompressed digital audio to be embbedded as well.

SET CARP   Shorthand phrase for Set carpenter, or the crew/personnel in charge of the set design, construction or transportation of carts and scenic pieces.

SHACKLE (RIGGING)
This steel device is the primary mechanism to link all manner of rigging systems. A shackle is a "u-shaped" piece of steel with a locking twist pin on the bottom of the hook.[61]

SHADE
Open or close the irises of a camera either remotely via the CCU or on camera by the camera operator.

SHADER
The person that adjusts the iris levels on the cameras from the control room via a CCU.

SHEAVE BLOCK
The grooved wheel of a pulley system that is often used with a rope for rigging or hoisting an object. These often need rope locks in order to be effective and safe. [62]

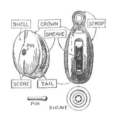

SHOT
A specified angle, or continuous piece of film.

SHOTGUN MICROPHONE
This highly directional microphone is used to achieve precise control of the source of sound.[63]

SHOW BLACKS
This is a term referring to the dress code of a show, meaning all crew and backstage members should wear as much completely black clothing as possible. Often it is frowned upon to have any logos, textures or non-black clothing when you are working backstage during an event. Corporate events "show blacks" often require black button down shirts and dress pants to look more professional.

SHRINK WRAP A material that constricts with heat or pressure.

SHUTTER Metal plates inside a leko or ellipsoidal light to block light in specific patterns.

SHUTTER SPEED The length of time that a single frame is exposed for. Slower shutter speeds allow more light to enter the camera, but allow for motion blur.

SIGNAL FLOW A diagram or chart that shows the path of cables that a system needs in order to be show-ready. This is usually designed by the EIC and/or PM

SINGLE PHASE A power source of alternating current where there is alternating voltage pattern.

SINGLE-MAN LIFT A vertical mast lift design for use with a single operator that often have outriggers to counter-balance the weight. Also known as a bucket lift.

SKID A slang term for pallet, or the wooden platform used to ship cases or goods.[64]

SKIRT The curtain that is attached to a deck to cover the under structures of a stage or riser.

SLED This is an attachment to the lens of a camera allowing for better support of a large-format lens or box lens.

SLING (RADIO) The slang term for a shoulder-mounted microphone and speaker for two-way radios. Also referred to as a Biscuit or Puck.

SLOW MOTION Also referred to as "slow-mo" or "overcranking." Process of shooting at a faster frame rate than the object will be played back in, giving the perception of an object that is moving slower than normal.

SMAART   A set of software tools used for audio measurement and analysis commonly used for sound system optimization.

SMPTE TIME CODE   Stands for "Society of Motion Picture and Television Engineers" and used as a signal to lock certain aspects of the live production together in an effort to be synchronized in their cues, or use.

SNAKE   A multi-channel audio cable intended for use with microphone level signals and/or line level signals.

SNAP ZOOM   A quick zoom of your subject, usually performed by manually adjusting the focal ring.

SOCAPEX   An electrical connector that carries 19-pins and allows for multiple power lines to be run within one single cable. This brand of connector is a standard in stage lighting and video technology whereby multiple electrical signals are needed in one place. There are also Socapex breakouts to go from Socapex to edison, stage pin, and power-con. Also referred to as Multiplex.

SOFFIT   A lowered section or portion of the ceiling in a ballroom, exhibit hall or event space.

SOFT   A term used by a video director to let a camera operator know that their shot is out of focus or not as sharp as it could be.

SOFT GOODS   The generic term to sum up fabric, curtain, drapes or other textile material.

SOLO   The button on an audio console that allows you to isolate the sound from one channel, or multiple, in your headphones, monitors or meters.

SPAN   A term used in rigging to identify the distance between two hang points or ground supported points.

SPANSET (RIGGING)	A round sling made up of nylon strands inside a polyester cover that is capable of hanging heavy weight loads. A spanset is almost identical to a Gac Flex (gac), except that a Gac Flex uses galvanized aircraft cable rather than nylon fiber.
SPARKY	Slang term for electrician.
SPEED	A term used to identify that cameras or record decks are running, giving confidence to the director that they may begin the scene or live shoot.
SPIKE	A marker on a stage to identify for stage managers where to place a specific set piece or prop, often identified by a colored piece of tape. Also referred to as a mark.
SPL	Stands for "Sound Pressure Level." A measure of how loud a sound is at a specific place and is measured in decibels.
SPL METER	A handheld device that shows the measurement of SPL or sound pressure level in an environment.
SPLIT SCREEN	A phrase used to identify that two cameras or two graphics will be combined on a single screen.
SPOT OP	The crew member or operator of a follow spot
SPOTLIGHT	Another term for a follow spot, or a powerful lighting instrument that can be moved by an operator to provide a focused, extremely bright beam, onto the performance  area highlighting the area it is aimed.[65]

STAGE BOX   This is a box with various connectors and connects to the
sub snake.[66]

STAGE LEFT   The left side of an auditorium or venue determined by the perspective of the stage looking
at the audience.

STAGE PLOT   A diagram or drawing showing where key set
pieces, personnel or talent need to be placed
on a stage deck.

STAGE RIGHT

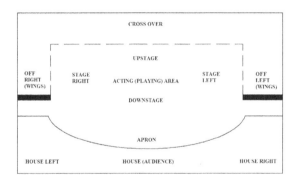

The right side of an auditorium or venue determined by the perspective of the stage looking
at the audience.[67]

STANDBY   A phrase used to let a camera operator be
alerted that their shot may be taken by the
director.

STATIC SHOT   A non-moving, still camera shot of your subject.

STEADICAM

A camera that is attached to a camera operator via a mechanical harness to reduce or eliminate the unsteadiness of a operator's motion, most specifically walking or running.[68]

STEWARD (UNION)

The union crew leader on a job to oversee the various groups of union members. In some states/locations there are working stewards and in others there are non-working stewards

STILL STORE

The ability to store a still image in a switcher or processor to be used as a source.

STINGER

A slang term for extension cord. Most often referred to a single "hot" extension that is laying around for occasional use.

STINGER (RIGGING)

A length of steel cable used to extend the motor chain so it can reach the overhead suspension point

STROBE

A lighting instrument that is capable of extremely bright and short bursts of light.

STOCK

Pre made music, video, images or effects that are purchased on a third party website with royalty free use.

STRIKE

The term used for breaking down a show or removing something from a stage, scene or set. Ex. "Let's strike that table", or "when does strike begins after the show ends?"

STRIP LIGHT

A row of small lights or LEDs mounted in a horizontal line in a single fixture. Also known as "Batten light" or "Bar Light."

SUB

Shorten phrase for Subwoofer.

SUB SNAKE — This is a smaller form of an audio snake used for regional runs, often to areas of a stage with musicians or positions with multiple inputs. The sub snake will have a fan-out on one end and a stage box or dropbox on the stage side.

SUPERCARDIOID MICROPHONE — The directional microphone that has a more defined polar/pickup pattern where it is most sensitive to an on-axis audio source. Also known as a hypercardioid microphone.

SWAG — Short for "Stuff we all get" and is a live production term to refer to the t-shirts, jackets, bags, or other merchandise that crew members may get from being part of a live show.

SWITCHER — Takes the inputs from sources and allows you to go back and forth between inputs. Can also be referred to as a technical director.[69]

SWR (RIGGING) — Abbreviation for Steel Wire Rope and used in rigging.

SYNC TEST — The procedure to identify if audio and video lines are in sync with one another. Often this is a video clip of a ball or dot moving left to right making a sound at a specific point to allow for easy tweaking of delays on either end. Checking sync is vital before any event.

T

TAILS This is the common term for the cables to connect directly to a distribution box, electrical box or other connection at the venue or generator, to get to the traveling or rented distro for the show.

TALKBACK MIC Any microphone where the engineer can talk into the monitors or ears of the performers on stage.

TALLY LIGHT A small light on a video camera which turns on when recording is in progress. In multi camera situations; a light on a camera, or in it's viewfinder, which turns on when the camera is live.

TEAMSTER The union member that handles logistics of all the in and out elements of a show or exhibit for non-electrical functions.

TEASER This is the curtain on a stage that runs horizontally along the top of a stage to provide a top border and reduce the height of the stage. A teaser almost always covers the lighting and electrical equipment hanging above the stage.

TECH DRAPE Black masking fabric to cover the height of FOH (front of house) cables, tables, and equipment to prevent being seen from the audience.

TECHNICAL DIRECTOR (TD) This is the person that works with the camera director to often control the actual buttons on the video switcher.

TELEPROMPTER A video monitor that displays notes visible only to the speaker and/or band.[70]

THEATRE-STYLE This seating arrangement is often fixed or temporary, but all chairs are set in rows with aisles facing the main stage. This is the most popular style of seating arrangement for lectures, performances, keynote addresses and/or product launches.

THIRD PACK Case size of 30" wide to allow for three cases to go side-by-side in a 90" truck to fill the width. Each "third pack" case takes up one-third of the width of a truck.

THREE PHASE A power source of alternating current where there is three alternating voltage patterns, creating a more efficient and reliable power supply.

THROW RATIO (OR LENS RATIO) A formula used to calculate how far a projector needs to be away from the screen and is usually divided by screen width.

THRUST A stage deck that extends into the audience, allowing for a runway or extruded, isolated section.

TIE IN A power feed obtained by temporarily clipping on the main service of a location. Though this methodology is illegal in many areas, often it is only referred to as a slang word for connecting cam-lock into a breaker panel for an outside power distributor.

TIGHTEN UP   A phrase used by a camera director to get the camera operator to zoom in on the subject slightly, referring that your shot is too wide.

TILT   Vertical camera movement, adjusting the framing up and down.

TILT LOCK   This adjustment prevents the tripod head from making up and down movement when a camera operator isn't present or if tilt is not needed by the camera operator.

TIMECODE   An indexing system that assigns a time value to individual frames of a film or video, or sections of an audio file.

TOTEM   The term used when truss is attached to a base plate and used as a vertical column. Also referred to as truss tower.[71]

TRACKING (TYPOGRAPHY)   The horizontal space between groups of characters in typography. Often this is associated with the spacing between words, but can often be grouped in alternative methods. This is most helpful in justified paragraph formatting to avoid hyphenated words splitting the lines.

TRACKS (MUSIC)   Often a backing set of sounds or music that accompanies the band. This may include a click-track that needs to only be heard by musicians or loop-tracks that will be piped into the PA System alongside the band.

TRANSITION   A controlled change from one video input to another video input or black. The change can occur through a wipe, cut, dissolve or "DVE" effect.

TRAVELER A curtain that opens horizontally. The most common traveler is the front curtain, and most theatres have multiple traveler curtains to divide the sections of the stage.

TRIM The predetermined height of a set piece, curtain, speaker box or screen to identify it's "in-show" position.

TRIPOD A three-legged stand for mounting equipment like cameras.

TRIPOD HEAD The top part of a tripod that lets you mount a camera to it, and allows for tilt and pan smoothly.[72]

TRITAP An electrical adapter that has three female edison plugs and one male edison connector to expand the number of edison outlets.

TRS CONNECTOR A type of connector with three connections: tip, ring, and sleeve. Often TRS is for balanced, or stereo connections.

TRUMPET TOOL A specific tool to plug a BNC connector in and out of tight or hard-to-reach outlets.

TRUNK A road case that does not have dividers or partitions and can carry items loose. Most often used for cables, or other cases.

TRUSS Metal grid-like structure usually suspended above the stage or audience that is used to hang lights, sound, or other equipment from.[73]

TRUSS TOOLS A pair of tools consisting of a combination of 15/16" socket wrench and/or combination wrench, to fit the standard truss bolts in event production.

TRUSS TOWER The term used when truss is attached to a base plate and used as a vertical column. Also referred to as a totem.[74]

TS CONNECTOR A type of connector with two connections: tip and sleeve. Often TS connectors are for unbalanced outputs.

TURNAROUND An adapter or converter that has two of the same gender as a way of connecting two ports, cables or signals into the same gender.

TWEETER The part of a speaker that handles the highest frequencies of an audio signal.

TWIST LOCK A cable connector that locks when twisted. The connector usually has a L-shaped prong.[75]

U

ULTRA HD Also known as 4k by many, but it's a resolution that is four times the size of a 1920x1080 image with 3840 pixels across and 2160 pixels down.

UNBALANCED AUDIO An audio signal which consists of one "hot" signal plus the shield.

UNDERCRANKING The process of slowing the frame rate of a camera down, so that when played back, it appears to be playing in fast motion.

UNDERSCAN Decreasing the size of your output to make the source be seen entirely on your screen.

UP LIGHT The process of using an LED or par light to cascade upward on a wall, fabric or set piece to create an indirect reflection of light.

UP RIGGER The crew member that is in the "air" when rigging and secures the rigging equipment to the beams or grid above the ground.

UP/DOWN/CROSS CONVERTER A digital video processor that converts one video format to another. Typically they are used to convert SD video to HD, HD to SD, or convert between HD formats. Up/Down/Cross converters can be either built into a switcher input or be a standalone unit.

UPSTAGE The areas of stage furthest away from an audience.

V

VALENCE   A short fabric or curtain to cover the top section of a stage or screen.

VECTORSCOPE   A tool used to measure chroma in video systems[76]

VELOUR   A common black fabric used for drapery, or curtains, in the live event world. This drape has a velvet like front providing a deep black look on camera.

VIDEO   Any medium which displays moving images electronically. The electrical signal produced by a television camera, character generator or other image source.

VIDEO ENGINEER   A technician that is responsible for controlling the iris and color balancing of cameras, and oversees calibration of video equipment.

VIDEO VILLAGE   This is the location of video switching gear, flypack, and operators, usually back stage or in another room. This is a phrase that is most often used in temporary productions and not permanent installs. Also referred to as video world

VIEWFINDER   A component of video, television and film cameras with a small screen that displays the camera output.

VIRTUAL REALITY (VR) A simulated experience with visual technology that can be similar or completely different from reality, causing a virtual representation often viewed through glasses or projected lenses covering the eyes.

VJ Abbreviation for video jockey. This is the crew member who mixes live video clips, effects and feeds into a video wall, or surface for the purpose of entertainment, backdrop or engagement. This is the video version of a lighting operator with visual media. Often they use a tool to allow for on-the-fly manipulation of video/media elements.

VOICE OF GOD This refers to someone announcing over a PA but isn't shown publicly doing so. Voice of God usually is a good fit for doing guest speaker introductions, instructing people to take their seats, or informing a crowd of a general update. This is also known as a "VOG"

VOMITORY OR VOMITORIUM An entrance to the theater under an area of elevated audience seating, like the locker room tunnel in a basketball arena or football stadium. Name refers to ancient Roman architectural design. Most commonly known as a "vom."

VU METER A meter designed to measure audio level in volume units which generally correspond to perceived loudness.[77]

W

WANDS Short for "magnetic wands" and used by security personnel to determine if the patron or person being scanned has any metal on them.

WARPING A technique in projection alignment where you have the ability to modify specific areas of your image to fit an abnormal shape, screen or surface. You can literally "warp" the image in any customized manner, by adjusting points on a grid.

WASH The general fill of light on a stage or specific area of the stage. A good wash has an even balance of brightness and color, creating a seamless flood of light across the specified area.

WAVEFORM MONITOR Designed to display the waveforms of video signals. Used to monitor signal strength, sync timing, etc.

WEDGE A slang term for an audio monitor on stage.

WET AUDIO The term used referring to processed or effected audio signal.

WHITE BALANCE A camera function which gives a reference to "true white" in order for the camera to interpret all colors correctly. This process helps make sure all cameras match color temperatures in a multi-camera shoot.

WHITE NOISE A signal having an equal amount of energy per hertz.

WIDE SCREEN   Generally refers to any aspect ratio greater than 4:3.

WIDE SHOT   A framing term, meaning a camera shot which shows the whole of the subject.

WINCH MOTOR   A system that uses a spool of cable or rope to lift something. These also operate at a lower volume and can move at a faster speed than a chain hoist.

WINGS   The area just off stage where a cast and crew members in theatre enter and exit.

WIPE   A video transition in which parts of one shot are successively replaced by equivalent parts of the next shot.

WISIWYG   The abbreviation of "what you see is what you get" referring to a type of lighting or video design / programming software to visualize a set or production design prior to installing it in a temporary or permanent space.

WORKBOX   A box, container or case full of personal tools or adapters often used in a live environment or production space.

WRAP   1. The term in rigging to cover or secure something. You would often "wrap a truss" with the spanset.
2. The term used to define the end of a work day. Ex: "That's a wrap, we'll see you guys tomorrow!"

X-Z

XLR   A lockable connector, available with various numbers
of pins (most common being
3-pin).[78]

YELLOW JACKET   A brand name hard cover for cables used to
protect cable from damage and to minimize trip
hazards. Also referred to as cable ramp.

ZEBRA STRIPES   A feature on professional cameras, which places
diagonal lines across any over-exposed parts of
the picture in the viewfinder. These stripes will
not show on the output/recorded picture, they
are only there as a guide for the camera operator.

ZOOM   Framing movement, in which the focal length of
the zoom lens is altered to make the subject appear closer to, or further away from the camera.
Note that this effect is similar, but not the same
as moving the camera itself closer to or further
away from the subject.

CONNECTORS

Audio Connectors

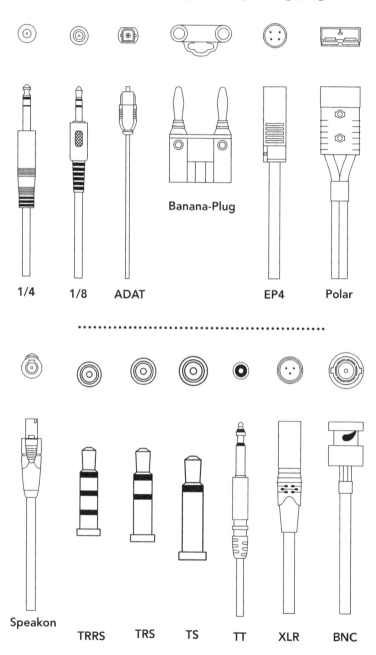

Banana-Plug

1/4   1/8   ADAT   EP4   Polar

Speakon   TRRS   TRS   TS   TT   XLR   BNC

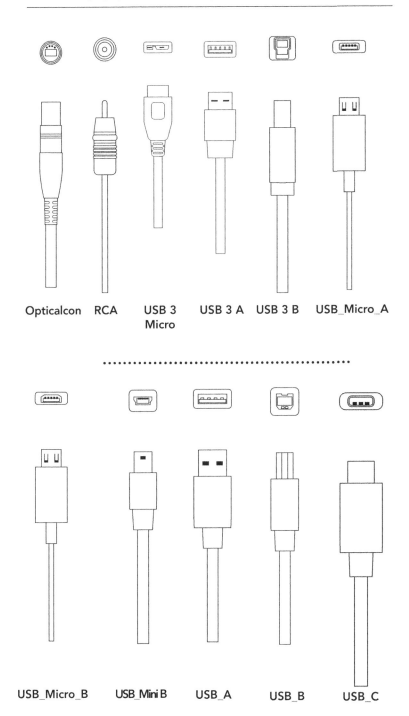

Opticalcon RCA USB 3 Micro USB 3 A USB 3 B USB_Micro_A

USB_Micro_B USB_Mini B USB_A USB_B USB_C

LIGHTING CONNECTORS

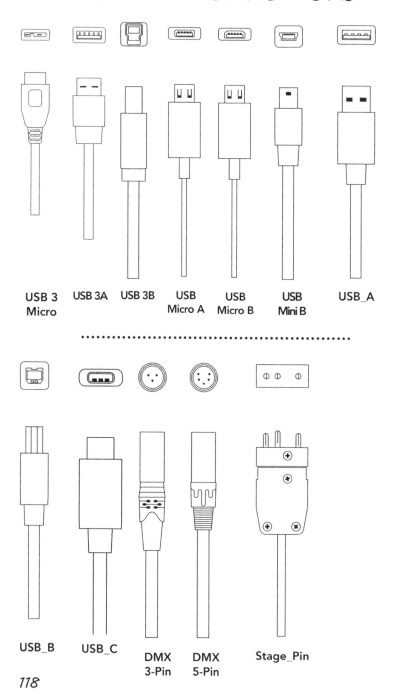

USB 3
Micro

USB 3A

USB 3B

USB
Micro A

USB
Micro B

USB
Mini B

USB_A

USB_B

USB_C

DMX
3-Pin

DMX
5-Pin

Stage_Pin

Network Connectors

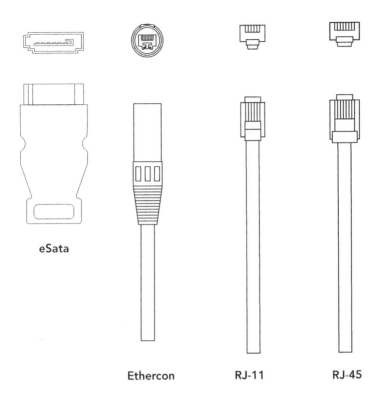

eSata

Ethercon   RJ-11   RJ-45

Power Connectors

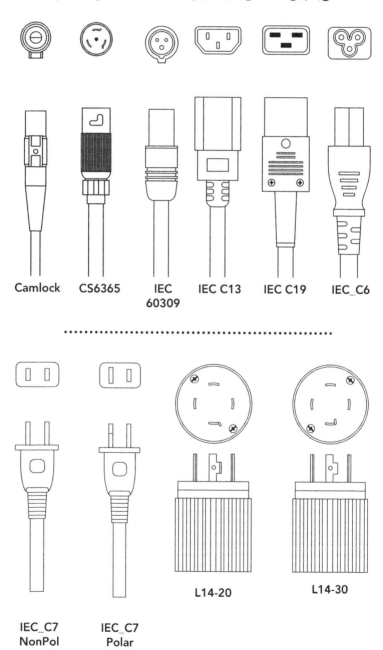

Camlock   CS6365   IEC 60309   IEC C13   IEC C19   IEC_C6

IEC_C7 NonPol   IEC_C7 Polar   L14-20   L14-30

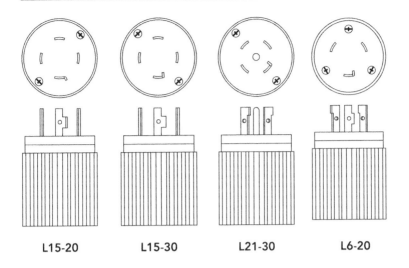

L15-20   L15-30   L21-30   L6-20

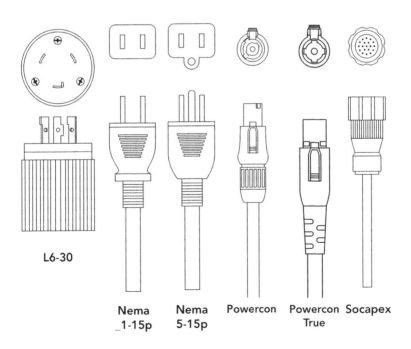

L6-30

Nema   Nema   Powercon   Powercon   Socapex
_1-15p   5-15p   True

Video Connectors

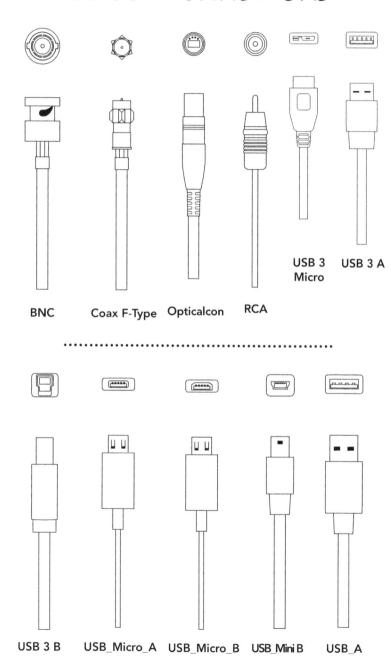

BNC Coax F-Type Opticalcon RCA USB 3 Micro USB 3 A

USB 3 B USB_Micro_A USB_Micro_B USB_Mini B USB_A

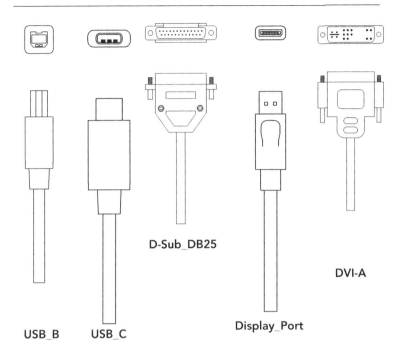

D-Sub_DB25

DVI-A

USB_B   USB_C

Display_Port

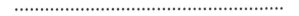

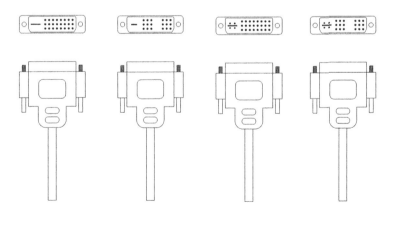

DVI-D_Dual   DVI-D_Single   DVI-I_Dual   DVI-I_Single

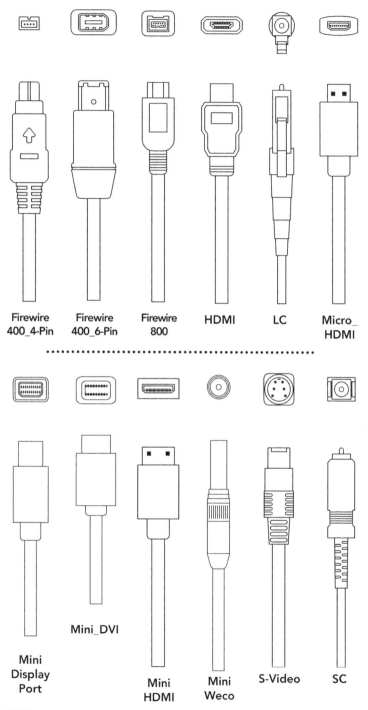

Firewire 400_4-Pin

Firewire 400_6-Pin

Firewire 800

HDMI

LC

Micro_ HDMI

Mini Display Port

Mini_DVI

Mini HDMI

Mini Weco

S-Video

SC

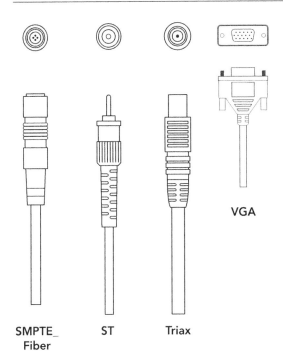

SMPTE_   ST   Triax
Fiber

VGA

PHOTO CREDITS

1   Public doman.
2   © Diagram Copyright 2020, Luke McElroy.
3   © Copyright 2008, Douglas Muth
4   © Copyright 2004, Henry Nelson, Wichita Kansas, USA.
5   Public domain.
6   © Copyright 2006, Nicolas Esposito
7   © Copyright 2011. AV Hire London via Flickr.
8   Public domain.
9   © Copyright 2013, Swift.Hg via Wikipedia.
10   © Copyright 2008, Norman Ferguson and Mary-Claire.
11   © Copyright 2019, SALT Conferences.
12   © Copyright 2019, ERab123 via Wikipedia.
13   © Copyright 2011, Lucas Bosch via Wikipedia.
14   © Copyright 2012, Arild Vågen via Wikipedia.
15   © Copyright 2015, Joseph T Wilkinson via Wikipedia.
16   © Copyright 2017, Fructibus.
17   © Copyright 2008, Vlad XXX (Silverxxx) via Wikipedia.
18   © Copyright 2017, Robert Harker via Wikipedia.
19   © Copyright 2008, Sean Devine via Wikipedia.
20   Public domain.
21   © Copyright 2011, SMCgear via Wikipedia.
22   © Copyright 2010, DJSparky via Wikipedia.
23   © Copyright 2005, Hella via German Language Wikipedia.
24   © Copyright 2007, Denelson83 via Wikipedia.
25   Public domain.
26   © Copyright 2007, Bene via Wikipedia.
27   Public domain.
28   © Copyright 2017, Robert Harker via Wikipedia.
29   © Copyright 2010, Ildar Sagdejev via Flickr.
30   © Copyright 2018, Luke McElroy
31   © Copyright 2010, DJSparky via Wikipedia
32   Public domain
33   © Copyright 2010, Samuel M Livingson via Flickr.
34   © Copyright 2020, Christian D Fielding via Wikipedia.

Looking for additional resources? SALT has curated some of the best free resources to help you with your daily workload. We offer everything from lyric templates to event planning checklists, design program shortcuts to filmmaker resources, and much more! Head over to SALTcommunity.com/free-resources to download all these amazing resources!

ABOUT THE AUTHORS

CARL BARNHILL is a creative entrepreneur, motion designer and author. He is the Owner and Creative Director of [twelve:thirty]media, a company that serves organizations all over the world through motion graphics and coaching. He is the author of *The Ultimate Production Team Handbook*. You can find him in Columbia, South Carolina with his wife, Katie and two sons, Jacob and Wesley.

LUKE MCELROY is the founder of Orange Thread Media, the parent company to Orange Thread Live Events. Through his leadership, their work has been seen around the world through American Idol, Blake Shelton, Super Bowl and the countless other events. Luke is also the author of three other books, most recently Creative Potential. He and his wife Tricia live in Nashville, Tennessee.

Made in the USA
Monee, IL
22 March 2021